THE WORLD OF THE RED-TAILED HAWK

A LIVING WORLD BOOK
John K. Terres, Editor

LIVING WORLD BOOKS
John K. Terres, Editor

THE WORLD OF THE
Red-tailed Hawk

TEXT AND PHOTOGRAPHS BY
G. RONALD AUSTING

J. B. LIPPINCOTT COMPANY
PHILADELPHIA AND NEW YORK

Contents

THE WORLD OF THE RED-TAILED HAWK

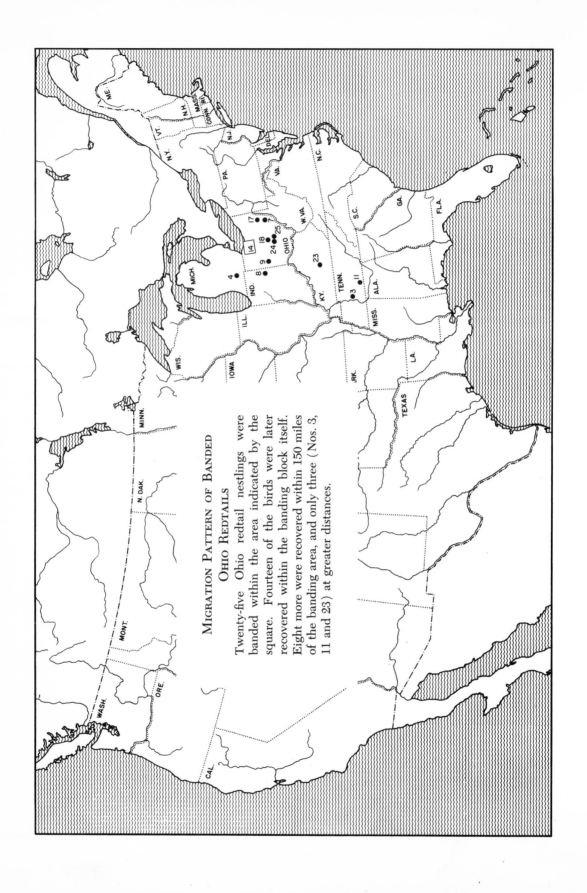

MIGRATION PATTERN OF BANDED
OHIO REDTAILS

Twenty-five Ohio redtail nestlings were banded within the area indicated by the square. Fourteen of the birds were later recovered within the banding block itself. Eight more were recovered within 150 miles of the banding area, and only three (Nos. 3, 11 and 23) at greater distances.

The Hawk Itself

OF ALL OUR HAWKS, the mighty red-tailed hawk is the one perhaps most familiar to those who have noticed a broad-winged, fan-tailed bird soaring lazily overhead on a breezy summer day. In the dead of winter, that same light-chested, motionless object can be seen perched atop a lonely tree snag, patiently scanning the surrounding fields with eyes so keen that they can detect the fleeting scurry of a meadow mouse a hundred yards away.

The range of the red-tailed hawk, *Buteo jamaicensis*, is quite extensive and covers much of North America, from coast to coast and from Alaska to the Dominican Republic. In the United States, one may expect to find it the year round, both as a breeding bird and as a winter resident.

Young redtails are strongly migratory during their first year. Some adults are migratory and travel great distances, as do birds hatched within the year. Others remain within the boundaries of a well-defined territory at all seasons. These individuals are mates for life and it is only upon the death of one of the pair that the survivor will take a new mate.

These pairs, which will be referred to as stable pairs throughout this text, occupy the choicest territories to be found, generally wild wooded areas that have yet to be altered by power shovels and bulldozers. These pairs are the nucleus of the species. If in the wake of our ever-exploding civilization we cannot somehow manage to save enough acreage to sustain a satisfactory number of stable pairs, the

11

extirpation of redtails from vast sections of their present range is inevitable.

Even today, as its numbers steadily decline, many of us are naive enough to take the redtail for granted. The species itself appears sufficiently adaptable to escape total extermination in the future, but its numbers will continue to decline as our own population increases. The day is fast approaching when the redtail will be absent from the daily check lists of amateur bird watchers.

Red-tailed hawks are the most robust and powerful of the North American buteos, a name given the red-tailed hawk, red-shouldered hawk and broad-winged hawk from their genus name, *Buteo*. The breeding range is also the most extensive, and such widespread geographical distribution has produced much variation in the bird, both in plumage color and in size. Typical redtails are the Midwestern birds of my own studies. The upperparts of adults are dark chocolate brown rather mottled with grayish-white; their underparts vary from nearly white to brown, with a broken band of brownish streaking on the upper breast and a heavier band across the abdomen. The undersurface of the wings shows dark-tipped feathers, and the tail is reddish brown with a narrow white tip and usually a dark subterminal band. Immature birds have upperparts that are duller brown than the adults', and their underparts are whiter; their tails are dull brown crossed by six to ten dark bands, and the abdominal band is usually more distinct than in adults. Adult males run from 19 to 22½ inches in length, with wingspreads of 46 to 50 inches; females vary from 21 to 25 inches in length, with wingspreads of 48 to 58 inches. Adult males average 36 to 40 ounces in weight; the females 48 to 56 ounces. Northeastern redtails are slightly smaller, and Florida birds are smallest of all.

In flight, the redtail cannot come close to matching the explosive dash of a Cooper's hawk, or the sustained drive of a peregrine falcon,

Immature peregrine (falcon).

12

Immature redtail.

Adult goshawk (accipiter).

because it is not built for speed like the accipiters and falcons. The long, wide wings of the redtail are designed for soaring, the characteristic manner of flight at which the buteos excel.

On calm days one seldom sees a redtail aloft for any length of time, except during the hot summer days when the birds encounter thermals and are able to rise with little effort. Ten- to twenty-mile-an-hour winds induce soaring, enabling the birds to remain in the air for extended periods with relative ease.

Although redtails usually do most of their hunting from a lookout perch, they also hunt from the air on favorable days when the wind is good. A hunting redtail is easy to spot and strongly resembles a hovering rough-legged hawk, when hunting the open fields. Immature redtails indulge in this hovering flight more often, possibly because they do not weigh as much as the adults and are more easily borne aloft on the wind. Though capable of spotting a mouse at a much greater distance, they seldom hunt from higher than 100 feet because the prey does not remain exposed for more than a few seconds and the attack must be quick.

Adults are often observed hunting on the wing along mountain ridges or other places where horizontal winds are deflected upward, creating updrafts. Here, the birds are able to hang motionless in the air with little more effort than when perching on a lookout post. Red-tails hunting from 400 feet or more above the ground are almost certainly on the lookout for larger prey, which, once spotted, cannot disappear so quickly as a mouse or shrew.

Since only about one out of ten redtails lives long enough to acquire the bright red tail, it is naturally well-educated in the school of survival. Buteos learn very quickly that it is useless to pursue flying birds under most conditions, and by the time they are mature they have learned their capabilities and limitations.

On rare occasions a redtail may attempt a falconlike swoop upon aerial prey, which sometimes ends in success. One redtail has been photographed capturing bats in this manner as they left their cave roost near dusk to begin their own hunting forays. Several years ago I watched an adult redtail plummet from 2,000 feet into a flock of pigeons that were flying low over a cornfield. This attack was unsuccessful, but the very fact that it was tried by an adult, experienced hawk leads me to believe it had been successful before.

Although pigeons are very seldom taken by redtails, this attempt may very likely have been planned strategy. The redtail, when still inexperienced, may have been successful the first time pigeon was tried, because the quarry may have mistaken the buteo for a falcon. Since a pigeon cannot outfly a large falcon that is determined to catch it, the only escape is to seek cover on the ground. Peregrine falcons

Under certain conditions bats have been captured by redtails.

will seldom follow their intended victim into cover, and pigeons seem to know this. The pigeon that took cover ahead of a plunging redtail would be easily captured if the cover was not too dense. It is possible that the redtail may have deliberately tried to deceive the pigeon flock by mimicking the falcon's swoop, thus forcing them to seek cover and freeze.

The top speed of a redtail in flight is somewhere between 35 and 40 miles an hour. I have clocked numerous adults with the special police speedometer in my patrol car, but can find no further references.

The World of the Red-tailed Hawk

When diving from high overhead, they can probably attain 120 m.p.h. This may seem a very fast rate for such a cumbersome bird, but it is merely the speed of gravitational pull for a falling object. Sky-diving parachutists attain this speed about 10 seconds after they leave the plane. A falcon, by way of comparison, may descend at nearly twice this speed, gaining the added momentum by pumping its wings on the way down.

Unlike many other hawks that are specialists in their dietary habits, the redtail is more of a general feeder and is able to prey upon a wide variety of animals, both in open country and in woodland. A scarcity of meadow mice, for example, will force such birds as marsh hawks and rough-legged hawks to move on, but the redtail can shift to rabbits or other larger animals that cannot be handled by the others. Redtails do not relish taking large prey, and when the choice is theirs will invariably choose the smaller and easier animals. This is especially true of the males which, being smaller than their mates, sometimes come to regret an encounter with the likes of a kicking rabbit. If the tussle is severe enough, the hawk never forgets it and will think twice before trying that particular quarry again, even when very hungry.

Some species of birds—vultures, for example—are credited with a good sense of smell, while other species seem to have none whatsoever. Although supporting evidence for so broad a generalization is lacking, it is probable that the majority of birds have a moderately developed olfactory sense. The red-tailed hawk is one of those species in which the sense of smell appears poorly developed, at least in helping to locate its prey.

Some years ago Dr. Frank M. Chapman of The American Museum of Natural History, New York City, hid some dead animals and tested the ability of the turkey vulture to locate decomposing animal matter by smell alone. As soon as the carcasses produced odors through advanced decay, numerous vultures were attracted to the spot of concealment. From this, one may conclude that smell is well developed

Female marsh hawk.

Rough-legged hawk.

Broad-winged hawk.

21

Cottontail (prey).

Gray squirrel (prey).

Chipmunk (prey).

Young woodchuck (prey).

Long-tailed shrew (prey).

Meadow mole (prey).

in vultures; but there is no way of knowing whether or not a redtail could detect similar odors, because hawks are not attracted to such putrid material as a source of food. It was later suggested that flies swarming around the carcass attracted the vultures, which associated their presence with a dead animal.

Mammals are well known for their highly developed sense of smell and use it to detect the approach of an enemy, and to locate food. Predatory animals usually have an even better olfactory sense, which enables them to follow their prey by the scent on the ground. But such a sense would be of little use in the air, where the scent would be only momentary and of no use at all in tracking. As ample compensation for their poor sense of smell, predatory birds, therefore, have evolved the superior visual acuity for which they are well known, and locate prey and detect enemies chiefly by sight.

The eyesight of an eagle is legendary, but the red-tailed hawk enjoys equally sharp vision. The eyes of a redtail are very large and occupy as much, or more, space in the head as the brain, each eye being almost as large in diameter as a full grown man's.

Eye of an albino redtail.

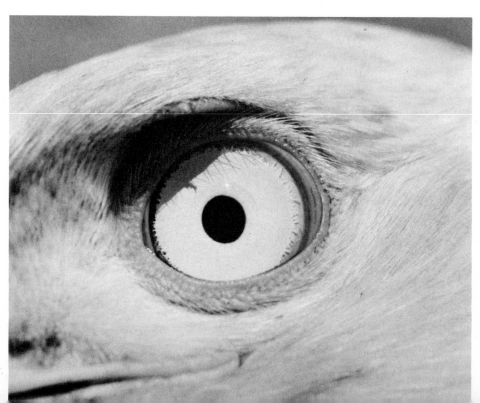

The Hawk Itself

The eyes of birds are classified as either flat, globose, or tubular. Flat eyes, characteristic of pigeons, have relatively slight convexities on their corneal surfaces, while the distance through the eye from cornea to retina is shorter than from the dorsal to ventral walls. In other words, flat eyes are broader than they are deep.

Globose and tubular eyes of the birds of prey have much greater corneal convexities. In globose eyes, either distance through them is about the same. In the tubular eyes of the red-tailed hawk, the distance between cornea and retina tends to be longer and the sides of the eye are noticeably concave, giving a tubular effect. This affords better vision at longer distances, an adaption with obvious advantages for such a bird. An interesting feature of the redtail's eye is the nictitating membrane, or "second eyelid." Although laymen frequently liken this membrane to a windshield—saying that it protects the hawk's eye as he flies through the rain, and so on—actually, its primary function is to cleanse and moisten the eye.

The redtail has both monocular and binocular vision. The binocular field of view covers about 50 degrees, considerably less than the flat-eyed birds, which may require the broader view to detect more numerous enemies. The hawk's eye, however, can adjust rapidly from distant viewing to close vision, as it must do in the pursuit of prey.

The ability of the redtail and other hawks to spot distant objects in the sky, visible to the human eye only through binoculars, is remarkable. A captive redtail makes an excellent "spotter" bird during the autumn hawk migration and will point out countless high-flying birds that otherwise would escape human detection. The captive merely cocks its head, to look up with one eye. The passing bird is usually watched for several seconds, and the spotter often cranes its neck, possibly to better judge the distance. It may also be true that such monocular vision in hawks functions like an adjustable telescope, with a zooming-in effect made possible by muscular action on the lens.

Although the hearing of birds is inferior to that in most mammals,

Melanistic adult.

it is nonetheless well-developed and plays an important role in their lives. Hunting, the chief occupation of the red-tailed hawk, is accomplished primarily by vision. However, the distress cries of most creatures often attract a nearby redtail, especially the high-pitched squealing of rabbits and other rodents. Since injured or handicapped animals are more readily captured, it is possible that hearing plays a more important function in relation to hunting than is generally realized.

Like most of the other buteos, the redtail exhibits wide variation in plumage coloration among individuals. Western birds tend strongly towards melanism, or excessive black pigment, and erythrism, or excessive red. Melanistic birds are affected primarily in the blackening

White redtail shortly after capture, showing extensive damage by lice.

of the contour plumage, with the tail and wings remaining close to normal. Black Eastern birds are rare.

Albinos are very rare and seem to be virtually unknown in the West. There have been numerous records of wholly white individuals from the East, and partial albinos are frequently reported. In 1960 some friends and I succeeded in trapping an all-white redtail near my home in southwestern Ohio. The entire plumage was white, although quite soiled and in worn condition. Feather lice of the Mallophaga group were present in abnormal numbers and appeared to have caused this damage. All exposed fleshy parts, including cere, feet, gape and eyelid rims were rich yellow. Talons and mandibles were light pinkish. Irises were whitish, tinged with pale yellow; retina was dark. The bird molted normally and all new feathers were immaculate. No other change in appearance was noted. Vision was excellent and voice normal.

There seems to be no other detailed description of an albino hawk in the literature, except that of a white red-shouldered hawk studied by Dr. Heinz Meng. This bird was found in a nest at Woodstock, New York, in 1952 and raised in captivity by Meng. Coloration was identical to that of the white redtail, except for pale blue irises. It is interesting to note that both these birds lived less than 3 years in cap-

Feather louse at work.

tivity. Both contracted fatal respiratory diseases, a rare cause of death in normal buteos.

In the wild state the red-tailed hawk is a very hardy species and where sufficient food is available it is unlikely to become infected. Captive redtails are similarly hardy and are more easily kept alive in zoos for long periods than most other birds of prey. Coccidiosis seems to be one disease that is more readily contracted if the bird is fed infected poultry, or is kept in a place where these fowl were housed. The sick hawk is readily cured by prompt treatment involving the use of antibiotics.

External parasites are usually harbored in small numbers. These include feather lice, and the blood-sucking Hippoboscid flies. There is one authentic case of tularemia having caused the death of a wild redtail. In general, there is still much to be learned about diseases and parasites of this hawk.

Most large predators, including red-tailed hawks, are not averse to killing chickens when hard pressed for food. This unfortunate habit has earned the misnomer "chicken hawk" for redtails in some areas. Even today, there remain a surprising number of people who refer to all hawks by this name.

It must be pointed out that chicken killing is not a universal habit of all redtails—or any other predator for that matter. When encountered, it is almost invariably being done by a young bird on the verge of starvation, making a last-ditch effort to survive; or a very old bird unable to compete any longer with its adult fellows.

Where free-ranging poultry roams at large over the hunting domain of redtails, some loss is bound to occur. But modern methods of production, in which the birds are pen-raised, eliminate such loss. Domestic fowl that do not venture away from the farmyard are relatively safe from redtails, even hungry ones.

My own experience with redtails in Ohio gives the adult birds a clean record, and I know of only a handful of cases in which the young

29

The World of the Red-tailed Hawk

hawks have been guilty of poaching. I have periodically checked upwards of 100 redtail nests and have yet to find a chicken feather in one. All these nests, it must be pointed out, were located in what I consider good habitat, with sufficient natural food to sustain the birds. Poultry was available near many nests but was not taken.

The general attitude of farmers in this area varies between total indifference, to affirmative enthusiasm about the presence of redtails in their woodlots. Few condemn the species outright any more, and many are outspoken in their praise of the hawk's mouse-catching ability.

In bygone years, it was the custom of biologists to educate the public about hawks through presentation of charts and tables that listed the feeding habits of various species of hawks. The birds were judged purely on the basis of their economic importance to man and were labeled good, bad, or harmless, according to the economic importance of the prey upon which they fed.

The feeding chart was the first step forward, but has long since outlived its usefulness. At best, the chart showed only the last meals of the birds examined. Many, if not most, of the hawks collected for these studies were obtained during fall or winter and were largely young ones, less wary and more easily killed with a shotgun. Their stomach contents were taken as *prima facie* evidence of a kill. But since redtails frequent areas where hunting pressure by man leaves many crippled pheasants and rabbits, and since wintering birds are not averse to dining on fresh roadside casualties, the biologists' tables and charts were filled with error. Without these studies, however, we could not have progressed to our present level of understanding and educational methods; so the laborious work of these men must be recognized as an important contribution.

Today, we know that the red-tailed hawk is neither good nor bad in its own community; it is *necessary* in its role of helping to keep in check the numbers of lesser creatures. The unfit are continuously weeded out through predation, thereby assuring a healthy breeding stock. The predator itself is controlled by the numbers of its prey, and could not survive if it depleted the breeding stock. Individual predators are often in the process of themselves being eliminated by starvation. Domestic fowl in these cases give them a new, but only temporary, lease on life.

Just as with other animals, hawks produce surpluses too, and the excess must be removed. It is very important that this occur naturally. The survivors of natural elimination will be those individuals best fitted in every way to carry on the species, the best assurance we can have that redtails will grace our skies in the future.

Spring

ALTHOUGH IN THE northern parts of its range the redtail is migratory and drifts southward in winter in search of a more abundant food supply, the mature breeding birds of the temperate zone are mostly stationary and do not vacate their summer haunts. Ohio adult redtails, for example, are chiefly permanent residents. They preside over the same range the year round, while their offspring, the immature birds of the year, often travel hundreds of miles south with the fall migration.

Other hawks, such as the closely related red-shouldered hawk, while still clad in the immature plumage of one-year-olds have been known to breed and successfully bring their young off the nest. Nesting redtails, however, are always at least two years old, since they invariably show the red tail of adult plumage.

Throughout the greater part of the United States where wilderness areas still exist to support a fairly constant wildlife population, the return of the birds to their old nest sites in spring is merely a short flight within their established home range. It is not the result of spring migration, as in the case of many other hawks. Being one of the largest of our hawks and slower to mature, the redtail is also slower to adjust to environmental changes.

Once a pair of redtails settle down to fit into an available niche in the wildlife community, they are inclined to remain in that area permanently and defend the range against other intruding redtails. They remain mated for life and enjoy considerably higher nesting

32

success than the redtails that are forced to settle in less suitable habitats.

With the advance of civilization bringing drastic changes to the countryside, the redtails become less stable and require a considerably larger range over which to hunt. With the approach of autumn and the gradual decline of available prey, many of these birds are forced to drift away to more productive hunting grounds, or even to migrate. Drifting tends to reduce hunting pressure in the summer range so that important prey species, such as meadow mice, may increase, and thus serve the birds upon their return to the nesting area in the spring. But this whole picture, under the disturbed conditions created by man, is so variable and complex that it becomes virtually impossible to speak generally about any except the more stable redtail pairs that occupy prime- and fringe-area haunts under wilderness conditions.

Although the Eastern red-tailed hawk has been selected to represent the species as a whole in this book, it may be said in general that redtails inhabit rather dry country, both hilly and flat. The red-shouldered hawk, by way of further comparison, tends to occupy moist or swampy areas.

Prime environmental conditions in southwestern Ohio may be observed in my study area. It is here that the Great Miami and Whitewater Rivers meet, soon to flow into the Ohio River. The terrain is roughly 70 per cent fertile river valley and 30 per cent well-drained hilly woodland. Where the woodlands are allowed to reach maturity, forming oak-hickory forests, the density of nesting redtails has been approximately one pair per square mile. In Miami-Whitewater Forest—the 1956-acre Hamilton County Park where I am employed as a park ranger—seven pairs have nested within its confines since I began observations in 1955.

It is interesting to note the comparatively high percentage of young redtails brought off the nest in this prime area, and the conspicuous absence of the red-shouldered hawk, which is the common

Nest overlooking the Whitewater River valley (Ohio).

breeding buteo in other parts of the country away from the river valleys. Where these two habitats meet to form a "fringe" area, both the redtail and the red-shoulder occur sparingly as breeding birds, but never in close proximity to each other. In such fringe areas the redtails tend to nest for one or two years in the same woodland, then vacate the area. It is not always obvious why they leave, but in many instances the red-shoulders set up housekeeping the following year. Occupancy of a given woodland often continues to switch back and forth between the two species every few years. The instability of both hawks in such a fringe area results in poorer nesting success than in the prime areas.

The redtails which attempt to establish a nesting territory in a fringe area are probably two- or three-year-olds engaging in a first or second nesting attempt. A limited food supply is often the deciding

34

Woodlot nest surrounded by cultivated fields (Indiana).

factor between success and failure. The inability of the male to provide for his incubating mate often forces her off the nest to hunt for herself. When her forays are prolonged, the eggs become chilled, or may be eaten by crows.

The territory of a fringe-area pair is, of necessity, quite a bit larger than that of a stable pair in prime habitat. The fringe birds may have to range over several square miles to find enough food, whereas in prime habitat a square mile or less will sustain a pair and their brood. It is tempting to think of the fringe birds as surplus breeding stock, biding their time, so to speak, until one or both are needed to replace old birds in the choice environment.

Being a powerful bird, the redtail seldom finds itself at the short end of any contest which may arise within its domicile. It commands respect from all other feathered members of the community—except

Great horned owl.

one: the great horned owl. The environmental requirements of the horned owl are basically the same as for the redtail. Both occupy the same areas and often the same nesting woodland. I have found both birds nesting simultaneously about 90 feet from each other.

Nesting success of the owl is, in many areas, largely dependent upon the presence of old redtail nests, especially where large decaying trees are scarce. Although the owl commonly nests in a snag or shallow cavity, it almost invariably appropriates the past year's nest of a redtail if one is available.

The resident redtails may often use the same nest for several successive years, then move a short distance to build a new one. It is not always clear just why the hawks change the nest site, especially in situations where they have enjoyed success in the old nest. The one obvious reason is that a pair of owls have taken over the old nest. Some owls use the hawks' previous nest with such regularity that the hawks are obliged to construct a new one each spring. However, since the

Great horned owl nests in snags; prefers redtail nest when available.

36

Great horned owls in redtail nest.

owls are very early nesters, the hawks have ample time to select a new site, and the nest is often ready for eggs as early as mid-February, three to four weeks before laying time.

The owls appropriate the old nest in the dead of winter or, even earlier, in November. Allowing 35 to 37 days for incubation and seven weeks in the nest, most young owls are out and flying before the earliest redtail eggs hatch; indeed, before some are even laid. Such a contrast in the timing of two predatory birds which occupy often identical eco-

Courtship display. The male is diving.

logical niches is difficult to understand. One reason may be that the young owls are much longer dependent upon the adults and require a longer training period before they acquire the skill of hunting successfully for themselves.

Being chiefly nocturnal, the owls apparently succeed in taking over the old nest without incident, while the hawks are asleep. I have often wondered if the hawks ever try to drive off the incubating owl when they find her sitting on what may well have been their own nursery. In some cases the events might prove very interesting, but unfortunately the question must remain unanswered.

Long before the official arrival of spring, during the first few mild, breezy days in mid-January, the old redtails become very much in evidence in the skies above their nesting woodlands. To the casual observer or week-end bird watcher, this marks the return of the birds to their old nesting sites. In reality, they may have been present all winter, perched motionless by the edge of a distant woodlot or beyond a ridge, patiently awaiting their prey.

The courtship flights of redtails in spring are thrilling spectacles to behold. I happen to be lucky enough to winess these flights daily, while on routine patrol in the park. By February 1, the courtship flight displays are well under way. Both birds mount higher and higher, to an elevation of a thousand feet or more. The male may then casually drift away in lazy circles. Oftentimes he dangles his legs as he continues to gain height. Then, without warning, he folds his wings and swoops directly at the female in a long dive. The instant before certain impact appears inevitable, he checks his speed, at the same time thrusting out his talons which seem almost to touch her back. He then "throws up" abruptly to gain a new position above her, carried there with comparative ease by the momentum attained in his dive. It is difficult to calculate the speed of the male in his swoop, but it certainly exceeds 100 miles an hour.

There are many variations of the courtship flight. Sometimes the female rolls over on her back and extends her talons to meet him and the two birds seem to clash briefly in mid-air. Occasionally a third bird, or even another pair, will join in the activities. Adult redtails seem to tolerate other adults, probably neighboring pairs, in the air above their ground territories in early spring, especially on favorable days when the winds induce easy flying. Ten- to twenty-mile-an-hour winds stimulate the flight by allowing the birds to remain aloft with a minimum of effort.

Spring

Immature birds are never permitted to join in the flight, and their chance arrival on the scene brings a swift response from the old birds which drive them away with deadly determination.

The whys and wherefores of pair formation remain largely a secret known only to the hawks. We do know, in general, that the birds remain mated for life. Certainly this is true of the stable, socially well-adjusted pairs which occupy the prime habitats and are not forced to separate during winter drift or migration. With the unstable pairs which occupy the secondary habitats it is difficult to be certain. It is likely, however, that some unstable pairs reunite at the previous nesting sites, especially where the habitat approaches a fringe-area type.

The bond which holds together a pair of old redtails is a strong one. Just last November, for example, I came upon a crippled adult male hawk on the ground and recognized him as one of the Ridge pair I had known for many years. The bone of one wing was shattered beyond repair, apparently from a rifle shot. As I reached down to pick him up, a shrill, angry cry echoed across the valley; the female had appeared from nowhere to challenge me. Hovering about a hundred feet overhead, she followed me as I walked back to the car with her mate in my arms. It was a pitiful drama as the devoted creature placed herself in this dangerous position in an attempt to distract me from her partner.

The female was left to occupy the old range alone and I observed her many times during the next few weeks. Then one day I noticed her perched with a new male, a dark colored individual characteristic of the wintering birds that drift into the area each year. Whether this male was picked from a number of wandering birds, or was simply the first to come across her range, it is impossible to say.

The behavior of redtails when disturbed by man is an interesting study in itself and subject to much variation. The old adults are among the shyest of creatures and are difficult to approach on foot closer than 100 yards. Where their range includes traveled highways they become

The World of the Red-tailed Hawk

conditioned to the passing of automobiles and tend to ignore them. Some adults will occupy a hunting perch within a hundred feet of a busy road. But if a car stops near by, they beat a hasty retreat. Immature birds, on the other hand, are remarkably tame, especially during winter. Unfortunately, they usually pay the penalty for such carelessness and very few of them live long enough to acquire the bright red tail of a second-year bird.

At the nest, the adults are often quite bold in their efforts to drive off an intruder. Unstable fringe-area pairs commonly vacate the immediate area of the nest at the approach of a man and will not return until after he is gone. But it is quite a different story when one invades the nest vicinity of a pair of old resident redtails. Instead of flying off in silence the female, when flushed off the nest, will most often circle above the intruder and scream defiantly. The male, from his hunting territory, is quick to respond to her cries of alarm, and together they will scream and circle overhead.

When one climbs the nest tree both birds become more excited, and are apt to begin swooping down at the climber in a most threatening manner. Upon his reaching the nest, their swoops may be within a few feet of his head, although as a rule only the female is so venturesome. The swoops are often made on half-folded wings, falcon style, at a fast rate of speed. The feathers vibrate through the air at this speed and produce a very audible rushing sound that is guaranteed to make one's heart pound.

With many pairs, the protective instinct at the nest is strongest when the young are recently hatched, and gradually declines as they grow older. However, there are other pairs which show great devotion in defending their nest site even before the eggs are laid, and up until the young depart.

The pair selected for photography to illustrate the home life of the redtail for this book were picked from among a dozen local pairs. Their nest was situated deep in a woodland in Miami-Whitewater For-

Climbing up to redtail nest.

est, where a permanent blind would be unlikely to attract attention. I had known this pair for several years. They were notorious head swoopers and devoted parents, and would be unlikely to suffer serious distraction because of my activities.

The nest was a new one, some 50 feet up in a black oak. It was situated in especially good light, from a photographer's standpoint. The only problem was the absence of a suitable nearby tree in which to construct the blind. I remedied this by erecting a 55-foot scaffolding tower 45 feet from the nest, the maximum distance at which I felt I could work with a 400-mm. telephoto lens to obtain crisp photographs. The tower was assembled over a period of three days, a few sections at a time, so the birds might adjust with a minimum of distraction to the sudden growth of such a monstrosity at their doorstep.

Female protests against climbers near her nest.

The job took six men a total of nearly 12 hours to complete. During these hours, in spite of all the hammering and clatter of metal, the female remained close at hand to watch every move. She spent her time either soaring close overhead or perched atop her favorite lookout post, about 300 feet from the nest. From this position, she enjoyed a commanding view of the surrounding area. Her continued screaming would usually bring the male from his hunting territory half a mile west of the nest site. He would appear high overhead and after a few rapid swoops would depart to resume his role as provider.

After we began taking pictures and our visits became regular, the

44

Tower and blind 45 feet from nest.

45

male seldom bothered to heed his mate's cries, but her own devotion remained constant. Even after the young had departed from the nest for good, but were still in the immediate vicinity, the old female continued to defend her nest. On the day we dismantled the tower, she protested just as strongly as she had at the beginning.

In the meantime, not only had the tower and blind been accepted by the family, but the young birds had used it as a temporary feeding platform.

Trying to present a general picture of the respective roles of the male and female redtail, where the sexes are alike in color and where size difference is not always readily apparent, is bound to be speculative; especially from the critical standpoint of an exacting scientist. It is only through careful, sustained periods of observation that the male and female can positively be identified and any really significant knowledge gained. Even then, it is often impossible to interpret the individual hawk's actions.

The actual selection of the nesting territory—a variable sized area somewhere within the home range that will be vigorously defended against all potential enemies—probably follows the ultimate selection of the nest site itself. The size of this territory within which a particular pair, especially the female, are inclined to challenge the presence of an interloper may vary according to topographical features. It may even vary from day to day and contract as the young grow older, according to the mood of the female. Availability of food, weather conditions, and the physical condition of the birds are other factors. The defended area further varies according to the type of intruder. Most redtails protest when a man comes within 300 yards of their nest.

Neighboring pairs of red-tailed hawks which occupy adjacent home ranges are usually tolerated high above, especially when weather conditions induce soaring. I have yet to witness anything but a playful skirmish between neighboring redtails in prime habitat, when one passes high over the other's ground range. Such birds are not inclined

Nest site (Ohio).

to trespass beyond the limits of their own established range on hunting forays, which brings about further mutual trust and allows them to live in peaceful coexistence. Immature hawks from the past year and wandering unmated adults are never tolerated anywhere near the nest, and in most cases are not permitted within the entire home range.

The nest itself is usually situated in mature timber, in a location that gives the incubating female a commanding view of the surrounding territory. In flat country, the nest is often set in a lofty crotch of the tallest tree available. There seems to be very little, if any, preference as

47

Nest site (Indiana).

to tree type. The same pair may be found in four or five different trees in as many years. Red-tailed hawks in other parts of the country build their nests in entirely different places. The Western birds often use the rocky cliffs in the mountainous areas, and occasionally utilize old nests of ravens, or even of the golden eagle. The desert birds commonly build in saguaro, the giant cactus of the southwestern United States.

The nest is large and bulky, and of very sturdy construction. The base is made of heavy sticks of up to a half inch in diameter and two feet long. The center depression which holds the eggs is carefully lined

48

Nest site overlooking golf course under construction—an insecure position.

with softer material—strips of inner bark from red cedar, grapevine, corn shucks, long grasses, and so on.

Both male and female participate in the construction of the nest, and the rough platform is ready for finishing touches within a very few days. The birds are very fussy and deliberate in shaping the center depression, and squat down on their breasts continuously as if to test its comfort. Wings, beak, feet and breast are all used to form the depression, with final shaping being left to the female. From this period on,

49

Typical nest.

which may be several weeks before the eggs are laid, the female spends much time alone on the nest, perched on the rim. Final touches are added, such as green sprigs from cedar, pine or hemlock. Some nests are scantily adorned; others profusely decorated. I once counted 42 pieces of red cedar foliage in a nest, each piece 6 to 12 inches long.

A typical nest measures about 30 inches across, with an inner depression 4 to 5 inches deep and in diameter roughly half the outside measurement, or 15 inches. The height of the nest from bottom to top, varies considerably, depending somewhat on where the nest is situated,

50

but is generally less than the diameter. Old nests that have been in use for several successive years may reach dimensions of 4 feet across and 3 feet high.

Ohio redtails lay either two or three eggs, perhaps more often three. In the East and South, the number is usually two, sometimes only one. In the West, sets of four are not uncommon, and even as many as five have been recorded. The egg is oval in shape, the shell finely granulated, without much gloss. The ground color is usually dull or dirty white, sometimes faintly bluish white, and occasionally greenish white. Some eggs are nearly immaculate, but most are more or less sparingly blotched in shades of dull reddish or yellowish browns. They are seldom so handsomely marked as the red-shouldered hawk's eggs. A series of eggs from a single female redtail tends to run true to type, as to shape, color, and markings, and even number. When the female of a pair is lost and the male takes a new mate, her eggs are usually of a different type from those of the old female.

Laying dates, of course, vary with latitude. Ohio birds usually have fresh clutches by March 20. Florida birds average several weeks earlier; Canadian birds several weeks later. Strangely enough, the smaller red-shouldered hawks in my region average a week earlier than the redtails.

Incubation usually lasts for 30 days, but may vary between 28 and 32 days, or even more. The eggs of a tight-sitting female will hatch earlier than those of a bird that leaves the nest for prolonged periods. It has been my experience that the female alone attends to incubation, but other observers have noted that both sexes share in this duty. When the female alone does the sitting, the male brings food to the nest for her. During mild weather the female may leave the nest for brief periods to hunt for herself in the immediate vicinity, but she seldom ventures beyond sight of the nest to the more distant hunting grounds of the male. By contrast, the red-shouldered hawks in this area share equally in incubation, one sitting while the other hunts.

The newly hatched redtail is an attractive little fellow, covered

51

Red-shouldered hawks, illustrating strong instincts of female to keep eggs warm during cold rain shower. Male refused to vacate his incubating position when female returned from hunting.

with soft, silky down, grayish white in color, and with long hairlike filaments on the head which stand erect. This first natal down is gradually reinforced, as the hawklet grows, by a whiter, woollier down. The hawklets are brooded almost constantly for the first few days, and thereafter according to the temperature. They become easily chilled at this early age and are highly susceptible to pneumonia.

The young birds remain in the nest, or in the nest tree at least, for 6 to 7 weeks. Even after they have left the tree they may return to roost in the nest for several days. The main flight feathers, primaries and secondaries, burst their sheaths at 15 to 17 days, closely followed

Hatching.

Half hour old.

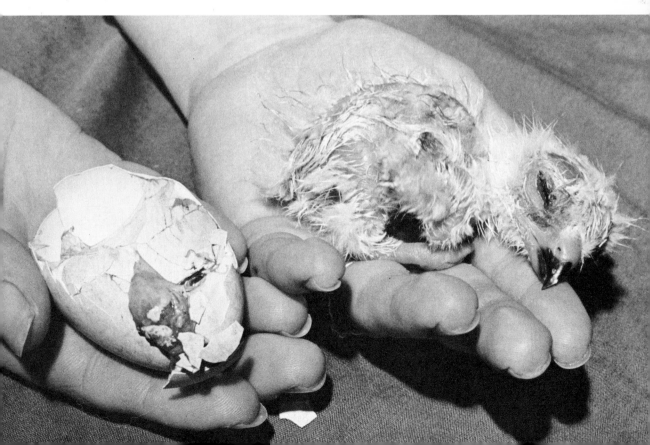

One day old. Note egg tooth near tip of upper mandible.

Three days old.

One week old.

Eleven-day-old hawklet fallen from nest.

by the tail feathers, or rectrices. Feathers of the mid-dorsal and scapular tracts become visible through the down at about 3 weeks. The last areas to be feathered are the thighs, belly, and head.

It is not uncommon, up to the age of 3 weeks, to discover one of the hawklets missing from the nest, sometimes lying dead on the ground below. During the early stages of photographing the nest pictured here, we arrived one morning to find one of the hawklets dead at the base of the nest tree, apparently killed by the fall. His age was 10 days. A few hours later, while inside the blind, we looked on helplessly as the surviving hawklet ventured too far over the rim of the nest and lost his footing. He struggled desperately to regain his balance, feebly flap-

Two weeks old.

Three-and-a-half weeks old.

57

ping his stubby wings. Just as it seemed his strength was exhausted, he somehow managed one last, determined surge that barely enabled him to recover and quickly scramble back to the center of the nest.

The female was on the nest at the time, but paid little attention to her hawklet's dilemma, much less offered any assistance. She had just fed him part of a mole, and after eating his fill he had begun to wander around the nest, to the front edge. It appeared to me that the female was confused by the absence of the dead hawklet, for she maintained her feeding stance on the nest, waiting to feed the other baby.

When the young birds fall, or are accidentally thrown from the nest, it is exceptional when the adults attempt to retrieve them. The only case I know of in which a redtail has been observed to carry a fallen youngster back to the nest is recorded by A. C. Bent, in his bulletin, "Life Histories of North American Birds of Prey," and seems reliable. Details are lacking, but the female did grasp the young bird in her talons and carry him back. It seems he was not injured in the fall.

The disappearance of young redtails from the nest while they are still quite small may occasionally be attributed to cannibalism, although this trait is more often observed in raptors that have large broods. With incubation often beginning with the laying of the first egg, the first to be hatched enjoys a distinct advantage over the others. Where food is scarce, the last of the brood to hatch seldom receives ample nourishment, because the larger nest mates are the first to be fed by the adults. The smaller birds soon become weak and may be eaten by their larger brothers and sisters when they approach death. Although cannibalism is not unknown with the redtail, the missing hawklets more often fall from the nest and are soon found by night-roaming predators, such as raccoons.

When first hatched, the downy young redtail is weak and helpless. Its head is quite large in proportion to the rest of the body, and several days must pass before the hawklet is able to hold up its head for any length of time. The task of breaking through the egg is ex-

Surviving youngster nearly suffered same fate as first hawklet; struggles to safety after near fall.

Female apparently removing parasite from head of young bird.

hausting to the little bird, and requires many hours. During its first day out of the egg the young bird is brooded continuously. The old bird is a gentle mother, very slow and deliberate in every movement, and infinitely cautious not to trample the young when she changes position.

Feeding usually begins on the second day, and is a slow process. The female carefully bites off tiny morsels from the prey and offers her garnished beak to the young birds, who instinctively pick at it.

Female inspects photographer's blind with piercing stare.

Female shading young bird from sun.

60

Female coaxing young bird to eat.

Female feeding young bird.

Male brings in mole for mate.

Female brings stick for nest.

Five weeks old.

They are feeble at first, but the old bird never lacks patience. If her offering turns out to be too large and the young bird has trouble in swallowing it, she carefully takes it back and swallows it herself, then offers a smaller bite. The feathers, or fur, and large bones are either discarded or partially eaten by the old bird.

The young birds do require a certain amount of calcium in their diet, and this they get from eating the smaller bones. Lack of calcium soon results in rickets, which is a common malady among pet hawks that have been taken from the nest and hand-reared on a straight beef diet. For proper nutrition, a young hawk must receive the "whole animal" diet it gets in the wild state.

At the age of two weeks the young hawk is strong enough to begin standing erect. Until this age it has been down on its heels. The young

Young exercise.

bird is wobbly at first, and often will remain standing only long enough to back to the edge of the nest and excrete over the side.

A week later finds the hawklet steadier on its feet and noticeably more active, walking around the nest and taking an interest in some of the things around it. The young bird may cock its head to watch a crawling insect, or see a warbler flitting about in the treetop. Its appetite increases too, and it now looks forward with anticipation to feeding time. At this age, to meet the greater demands of her brood, the female is obliged to venture away from the nest for longer periods to assist the male in hunting.

At four weeks of age the young hawk spends a great deal of time on its feet, and begins to indulge in frequent beating of its wings, to strengthen the muscles. It frequently dances about the nest, jumping

65

Playfully striking a stick (six weeks).

up and down while engaged in the flapping exercise. The hawklet also begins to stab out playfully with its talons, to grasp a stick or some other play toy in its cradle. The young hawk now possesses the necessary strength to partially feed itself when smaller prey is brought in by the adults.

At the age of five weeks the hawklet becomes more and more active, engaging in the wing-flapping and stabbing exercises at a much livelier tempo. It is now almost independent in the matter of tearing apart the prey and it begins to venture out of the nest, hopping and flapping up to nearby branches. The adults with larger broods now

66

Six-week-old hawklets mob female.

have their work cut out for them and must spend virtually the whole day hunting, to fill the needs of their ravenous children. When they do return to the nest with food, they are greedily mobbed by the young birds, which quickly seize the prey and fight over it with such struggles that the adult is sometimes forced to leave the nest.

At six weeks of age the young redtail is almost fully grown and

Just off the nest, young redtail watches parent soaring overhead.

about ready to leave the nest. It gains further strength and confidence in its ability to fly by flapping to more distant branches of nearby trees. Leaving the nest for good is usually a gradual process, and the young hawk may continue to use the nest as a feeding platform for another week or two. At seven to eight weeks of age, the young bird is completely grown, ready to test its broad wings on a thermal and follow its parents about to learn the fundamentals of hunting.

68

Summer

AFTER LEAVING the nest in June, the newly-fledged redtail has much to learn in a few short months. Even though young hawks hunt and kill through instinct, they must learn through experience how to catch their prey. Unless they catch it with methodical consistency, they are doomed to an early death by starvation. Once away from the care of the old birds, a substantial number of immature redtails perish by this primary natural check. Though the greatest toll is taken during the first fall and winter, starvation does occur during the dead of summer. This happens more often in secondary or fringe-area habitats, but is sometimes found in prime areas when the adults for some reason become slow in providing.

When first away from the nest the young redtails are very noisy and tend to make themselves conspicuous. Their incessant screaming and flapping about the nesting area during June and July makes no secret of their presence, as they impatiently await the return of their parents with food.

From what I have been able to observe, the fledglings make no attempts to follow the adults on hunting forays for the first few weeks, and when they finally do tag along the adults are prompt in losing them. Nothing can spoil a hunting expedition more effectively than the presence of a wailing, impatient youngster.

If the young birds are put through any sort of training program in learning to catch their prey, I doubt that it could be a very consistent one, because, as stated above, young redtails do this instinc-

Wailing immature bird, still dependent, makes his presence known.

tively. I have read accounts of adults teaching the young birds to strike prey by flying overhead and dropping the quarry so that the youngsters may strike it either in the air or on the ground. Having observed this action on a few occasions, I can only attribute it to the wisdom of the old birds, as it is a much more convenient and safer way to pass off food. This behavior is less likely to be seen when the brood consists of a single well-fed young bird, but the competition mounts in larger families and sometimes the young hawks literally mob the adult that takes to a perch with prey.

Over the past twenty years I have reared in captivity a dozen or so young redtails, including two that were hatched from eggs, and I cannot doubt that they hunt by instinct. These birds were never confined after fledging and were free to come and go as they pleased. They came to regard the immediate area around our house as their nesting territory and my wife and me as their parents.

Close-up of wailing immature bird.

The World of the Red-tailed Hawk

The first few birds I raised, and to which I tried to teach the fundamentals of hunting, remained dependent on a feeding hand fully as long as others that were fed in haste and with little ado. Once on the wing, the captive birds made little or no effort to chase potential quarry for the first two weeks. During this period they were very playful, if sufficiently well fed, and would chase dogs or cats with apparently deadly determination, only to strike lightly upon overtaking them. The young birds were almost constantly in evidence during this period, just as they would be in a nesting area.

As the young hawk gradually masters the powers of flight it gains in self-confidence. Its wailing ceases, along with much of the playfulness, and it soon settles down to its role as a hunter. This transition occurs in mid or late July in my area, about four weeks after the young birds are out of the nest. They then begin to accompany their parents to the favorite hunting areas. It is quite difficult, because of the heavy foliage at this time of year, to observe the activities of such a family group.

From my experiences with the captive birds that learned to hunt without a teacher I am led to conclude that this association with the parents at the choice hunting spots is not connected with any training program; rather, it places them in an area more favorable to their needs, with an abundant prey population. In such an area, their first hunting attempts are certain to be more successful than would be the case elsewhere, where prey might be scarce and their chances of catching it few.

The first hunting attempts of young redtails are naturally very clumsy, and to an observer often rather amusing. I once watched a determined young bird travel a great distance across an open field, intent upon a robin that was leisurely feeding in the short grass. The robin probably saw the hawk coming, but made no attempt to escape until the last moment, when it suddenly took to flight. While the redtail was striking empty ground, catching a foot full of sod for the effort, the robin was safely in the air.

The failure seemed to leave the inexperienced hawk completely baffled, for it remained perched on the ground a considerable time, a bit uncertain about just what to do next. Then, adding to its dilemma, the would-be victim took the offensive and became the attacker, darting back and forth above the hawk's head, once even pulling out a feather in passing. After a few such episodes, a young redtail learns the futility of chasing small birds.

This does not imply that henceforth small birds will be entirely lacking from the redtail's diet. Experience will teach the youngster how to recognize crippled or sickly birds, and young and inexperienced ones. Since small male redtails are somewhat more capable of maneuvering than are their larger sisters, they tend to try for any available small bird, while hesitating to try for some of the larger prey species which are more easily handled by the female.

To list the feeding menu of redtails in summer would be to name almost every living creature within their domain, from the larger insects to half-grown woodchucks. As general feeders, redtails are able to shift from one food staple to another, according to its abundance. Smaller mammals, especially meadow moles and ground squirrels, appear to be the most universally preferred items when they are available. In fact, when rodents are present in abnormal numbers older hawks often ignore other possible prey.

At the nest under my observation the male brought in a surprising number of moles during the early part of May. Ordinarily, these burrowing mammals are only occasionally captured by redtails. In this case, the male appeared to have discovered an area containing a high concentration of moles and was quick in fulfilling his role of weeding out the surplus. I have no idea how he went about catching the moles, whether he patiently awaited their occasional appearance through the

73

Blue-gray gnatcatcher attacks redtail.

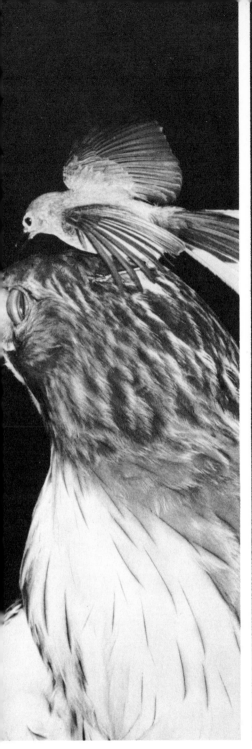

Male arrives with shrew.

ground, or simply struck at the moving burrow and tore it open to secure the victim. Chances are that the latter tactic was employed. Earlier in his life the redtail may have learned about the habits of moles through some chance meeting, perhaps when a mole surfaced.

Inexperience very often results in tragedy, which seems to be well illustrated in an account by E. D. Nauman, and is worth repeating: "A large Red-tailed Hawk . . . came out of the timber and leisurely flew around over the meadow, hovering over one point a moment for special inspection. Then he flew back to the woods again. A few min-

Male departs after bringing food.

utes later he flew out and hovered over the same place, then returned
to the woods as before. After having performed this round-trip movement several times, the hawk finally flew to this point and plunged
down into the meadow. Instantly there was a mighty commotion.
Hissing, flapping, spitting, caterwauling; and one could see feet, claws,
wings and tails whirling about just over the grass. The air was full
of fur and feathers for a few moments, then the hawk made his get-
away, and with feathers much ruffled flew for the timber as fast as
his wings could carry him. And an old gray tomcat went with great

77

bounds in equal haste for the farm buildings! Both Tommy and hawk were licked, but still able to go."

This account of a redtail attacking a cat is most interesting. But, regrettably, the report fails to include the age of the bird described, whether adult or immature, and does not mention the season, which leaves it more or less in the category of sensational reporting.

Lacking definite information, we may speculate that the individual was very likely immature. The season was probably fall or winter, but could have been summer. The hawk was obviously very hungry, otherwise it would not have attempted such a difficult capture. An old redtail, faced with starvation, would have struck the cat on the first or second pass and not wasted valuable energy through indecision. The determination of this bird, and at the same time its hesitancy, is typical of young redtails.

A rather amusing incident that took place in late July a few years ago further illustrates the inexperience of a young redtail. I was flying a trained prairie falcon in a large open valley in the park. The falcon was ringing low in large circles around me, perhaps a hundred feet above the ground. The redtail appeared from nowhere, dropping from overhead, and attempted to catch my falcon.

From his position above the falcon, the hawk seemed to hold a slight advantage for the moment, especially since the falcon ignored its presence until it closed to within 5 feet of her. Only then did she show her superiority in flight by an effortless burst of speed that quickly left the hawk far behind. Nevertheless my falcon was clearly impressed by the redtail's effort and has never forgotten the incident. Thereafter, whenever I exercised the prairie falcon around our yard, she lost no time in forcing the two captive, tethered redtails to vacate their perches —something she had never tried before. Goshawks and golden eagles received similar treatment, but generally not so vigorously as the redtails. No animosity was ever shown toward peregrine falcons. To this day, the prairie falcon refuses to fly if a redtail is anywhere in sight overhead. She will take a fast perch and remain there motionless until the hawk drifts out of her sight.

Like most birds of prey, redtails undergo one complete molt each year, which results in the acquisition of a whole new set of feathers. The immature birds change over to the adult plumage upon completion of the first molt. There is much variation among individuals with regard to the timing of the molt. Variations occur in the date of the first feathers dropped, the sequence or pattern of the change, and the duration of the molt. In addition, an individual does not necessarily follow the same schedule each year.

In spite of the tendency for the molt to be variable and irregular, it usually does follow a certain general pattern. The first molt is the most predictable of all and usually begins when the immature redtail approaches one year of age, early in the spring. The first feathers to be lost are often the two center tail feathers, along with the seventh primaries of the wings. As soon as the new feathers are well started, the adjacent old ones usually drop. Thus the molting of the tail and wings tends to progress in a rather well-defined symmetrical pattern.

The old feathers are actually pushed out by the new ones, and the corresponding primaries of each wing, most important of the flight feathers, are often dropped within a few hours of one another. The hawk thus maintains good balance in flight. Some birds fail to molt symmetrically and are somewhat handicapped for months at a time.

Like other birds, hawks have an oil gland near the base of the tail. They condition, or preen, their feathers by taking small amounts of the oily secretion on the beak and rubbing it over the entire plumage. The head feathers are treated by rubbing the head against the scapulars, after these have been freshly treated. Because hawks are so highly dependent upon flight as a means of securing food, they spend a great deal of time each day in the systematic preening of their feathers.

The contour feathers are replaced more or less at random, with

Adult preening.

perhaps those of the scapular tracts being the first. Final replacement almost invariably involves feathers of the head. Duration of the first molt is usually about five months, and the bird is in fresh adult plumage by early September.

Coincident with the first molt is the gradual darkening of the eyes and yellowing of the exposed parts. The irises eventually change to brown, but this is a prolonged process and may not be accomplished for several years. The tarsi and feet, cere and gape, change to yellow of varying shades, from the greenish or yellowish-green of the immature hawk. The yellow is usually much more pronounced in the lighter-plumaged birds—albinos are a rich, brilliant yellow in these areas—and tends to remain suppressed in very dark individuals and melanos. I once found a very old adult in the final throes of starvation. His exposed parts were all bluish-gray.

There seems to be a definite relationship between diet and the intensity of the yellow in captive redtails. Foods rich in carotene quickly brighten the yellow when it has faded through improper feeding. In most cases the feeding of egg yolk serves to brighten up

80

the yellow areas almost overnight. Among falconers, hawks with the richest color are considered the healthiest and are always the most coveted.

The second and subsequent molts grow increasingly more irregular among the resident adults of the temperate latitudes. Individuals of advanced age often show new feathers growing even in late winter. Generally, the adult molt does not begin until after the young are on the wing. It progresses rather slowly and is often incomplete. In some cases, the older the bird the more prolonged the molt. Very old birds may be in an almost constant state of molt, with more active feather replacement in summer, the season of prey abundance.

Although little is known about molt in migratory adults from the northern parts of the range, it is probably more rapid and perhaps more complete than in the birds of warmer climates. The shorter reproductive cycles of redtails and other species in a colder climate, as compared with birds of the same species that inhabit more temperate zones, may be a clue. Autumn and winter trapping of adults known to be migrants consistently reveals few new feathers growing, although a number of old, worn feathers may be present to show the molt was not quite complete. These northern birds differ somewhat in appearance from the local adults and are easily distinguished when in the hand.

The use of female hormones to stimulate and hasten the molting process has been accomplished with varying success by falconers, who wish to have their birds in full plumage as quickly as possible. Although nobody seems to have attempted it on female redtails, such hormones as progesterone and Norlutate have produced dramatic results in goshawk and peregrine falcon females, and presumably would stimulate the buteos as well.

For those of you who may find yourselves in possession of an orphaned or injured young redtail a word of caution: perhaps the greatest injustice such birds can suffer at human hands is to be fed an improper diet. I would hazard a guess that no less than 90 per cent of all young hawks obtained by boys, or even their parents, die of malnutrition before reaching the flying stage. A young hawk cannot survive on a diet of beef or hamburger.

From the day of hatching to the age of about three weeks a downy young hawklet must be kept warm constantly. A temperature of 85–90 degrees F. will be sufficient during this period, then may gradually be lowered for the next week until a minimum of 70 degrees is reached. Failure to keep the hawklet warm will result in its speedy death from pneumonia, which it can contract in a matter of hours.

In addition to warmth, the key to successful raising is proper feeding. There is hardly a substitute for natural food and it is imperative that the hawklet be fed the whole animal. This means every part of it, except fur or feathers, which in the wild are plucked from the prey by the female before feeding during the first few weeks. A young hawk that does not receive bone in its diet will soon develop weak legs from lack of calcium. Growing hawks digest the bones, but upon reaching the fledging stage most of the bones will be regurgitated in the form of a pellet each morning along with the other indigestible parts of the prey—feathers, fur, and so on. The best food for a young hawk is mice or sparrows. A young female redtail requires one mouse for each week of her age up to five weeks. Maximum requirement seldom exceeds five mice, but this is only a general guide. If the hawk is just hatched, the mouse must be cut into very small pieces and the larger bones should be broken.

After the hawklet is partially feathered and the outside temperature does not fall below 55–60 degrees F. at night, it should be placed in an artificial nest outside, preferably in a large tree with plenty of branches. A bushel basket filled with straw and sticks makes an ideal nest which can be nailed to the trunk of the tree. Some provision should be made to shelter the nest from rain, and from too much sun if the weather is hot. At five weeks the youngster can feed itself and fresh roadside kills of rabbits or squirrels serve as a convenient diet.

It happens all too often that after a young hawk is fledged and begins flying about the premises, its keeper decides the time has come to take a ride out in the country and release the hawk in the vicinity of a large wood. Although there is a possibility that a pair of resident redtails with young birds will adopt and feed the orphan, it is far more probable that the area is devoid of nesting hawks and the youngster is doomed to starvation.

About the only way to release a hand-reared bird to the wild state is to do it right from the yard nest. The procedure is very simple and requires only time. A young hawk will keep returning to be fed until it becomes self-sufficient. By early August most young redtails are catching their own food, and when successful will not return for a handout. It will not be long afterwards before the youngster abandons completely the foster parents.

Having a tame redtail flying about the yard can be quite a lively experience, since hand-reared nestlings soon lose all fear of man, and particularly delight in chasing domestic animals. Because of its size, a playful redtail can unintentionally inflict rather painful injury to a person with its needle-sharp talons.

A hungry bird, expecting to be fed, may fly down and innocently grip one's hand with its talons in anticipation. Some redtails come to associate the hand so closely with food that, when extremely hungry, they fail to differentiate between the two. Therefore, it is always wise to wear a leather glove, or gauntlet. By placing food in the artificial nest, preferably at a time and in such a manner that the hawk cannot see it in the hand, the association may gradually be broken. Obviously, it is better that a strong association be avoided from the beginning, if the hawk is to return to the wild state.

Although I never recommend that a redtail be taken deliberately for the sake of keeping an unusual pet, I know there are a number of people who do so anyway—a baby hawk seems to be a great temptation for youngsters. One must bear in mind that this species is protected by law in most states and it is illegal to hold a redtail captive without a permit. Enforcement of the hawk laws varies from state to state, even from county to county within a state, according to the personal views of the game warden. In the majority of cases at the time of writing, the bird is merely confiscated and the violator is released with a stern warning. At other times a token fine may be assessed; and on occasion a very severe one.

The best way to keep a redtail in good feather condition is by following the falconer's technique of fitting leather jesses to both legs. Both ends of the jesses are attached to one end of a free-turning swivel and a leather or nylon leash is fastened to the other end. The free end of the leash is then tied securely to the perch.

A few redtails have been kept successfully in roomy wire enclosures. But the majority of birds soon wreck themselves by repeatedly flying against the cage sides, not only breaking their feathers but also cutting themselves about the face. The cere—the soft part of a hawk's bill—is easily damaged on wire and once cut severely it seldom heals to its original smooth condition. Aside from the pain it suffers, a cere-scarred hawk loses much of its beauty and remains marked for life.

If a wire enclosure must be used, it should be constructed of the heaviest wire available. Chicken wire mesh is to be avoided in any case, because of its light gauge. Heavy welded fencing, 2 by 4 inches, may prove satisfactory, when the bird is tame and calm. Obviously a large cage is better than a small one. There is no such thing as a good cage size for hawks, but in the case of a redtail something like 6 by 6 by 15 feet should be the minimum.

Even though the birds most often used in falconry are falcons and accipiters, the red-tailed hawk is one of the few buteos that man

84

Trained redtail on ring perch.

has been able to train with fair success. The redtail stands out as one of the most spirited and determined of its genus and in the hands of a wise old falconer an especially aggressive bird can be effective in the taking of rabbits. Although a falconer could never expect to take as many rabbits with a redtail as he would with a goshawk, there is not too much difference between an exceptionally determined redtail and a goshawk that is unhappy with that type of quarry. A redtail will even plunge into heavy cover in pursuit of a rabbit. But the buteo lacks the speed for consistent success and is never so eager and quick off the fist as is the accomplished goshawk.

The most prominent role of the red-tailed hawk among falconry enthusiasts is as a trainer bird for young falconers, because its relatively calm disposition makes the redtail adapt more readily to this purpose than other, less common birds of the chase. "Training a hawk to hunt" is not falconry, as it has often been described. To begin with, hawks hunt by instinct. In the wild state, a redtail might kill a rabbit and eat it while a man watches from a distance of some 500 feet. If the man approaches, the hawk grows uneasy and may fly away if he comes within 300 feet. On the other hand, some birds are less afraid of man and will allow a closer approach. The training of a redtail, or any hawk, deals almost entirely with teaching it to overcome its natural fear of man, so as to tolerate his presence and allow itself to be retrieved, either after it has made a kill or after an unsuccessful flight. A hawk that is not tame will fly away when flown free, just like a wild one that is approached by man.

There are a number of pseudo-falconers who attempt to change the very nature of their birds by starving them into submission. It is impossible to change a hawk's nature, and a half-starved one is anything but a trained bird, even though it may appear so for the moment. Although it is true that even a well-fed and tame hawk will show little response to the commands of its trainer, a lean hawk might not have the strength to respond.

Since a fat hawk will not chase quarry, it must be kept in a certain physical condition similar to that of a wild hawk that is hungry and anxious to eat. Experienced falconers can judge the condition of their birds in many ways, but the novice must always use a scale and judge condition by watching the weight.

Summer

Before any young man undertakes to capture and train a hawk, he must first be sure that his activities will not violate the laws of the state in which he lives. He must also understand from the beginning that falconry is an occupation which demands a certain amount of daily tending that cannot be managed by assistants. A true falconer must learn to fit his own daily routine around the needs of his bird. Anyone unwilling to do this would not only be wasting his time but, more important, valuable birds. Falconry indeed becomes a way of life, and there are already enough people who make a mockery of this ancient, romantic sport.

A "passage" redtail makes the best trainer bird for the aspiring young falconer. This is a redtail less than a year old that is trapped during the fall migration. At this age its flying abilities are completely developed and the bird has gained a fair knowledge of how to outwit and capture prey. The passage redtail is easier to work with than the eyas that has been taken from the nest and hand-reared. Strange as it may seem, the eyas becomes too tame. The wild-caught individual always retains a certain amount of respect, or fear, of man, but the eyas tends to become so fearless that it eventually grows possessive. These birds are often so aggressive they will attack strangers who walk too close. Having no fear of man, they come to treat him as an intruder like any other animal whose presence is unwelcome.

Eyas hawks also develop such a close association between the trainer and food that they do not differentiate between the two when their appetites are keen. Most other birds of prey also behave in this manner, which can be somewhat amusing; but when a golden eagle is involved it ceases to be a laughing matter! However, a redtail is capable of inflicting alarming damage at times. A friend of mine once received a cut from an eyas redtail which required 13 stitches. This pronounced aggressiveness usually occurs about the time the eyas reaches the age of one year and is probably linked to territory defense.

The first steps in the training of a freshly caught passage hawk

The World of the Red-tailed Hawk

should begin as soon as possible after capture. These steps consist of teaching the frightened creature to overcome its natural fear of man and inducing it to eat. Only a patient man need venture any further, for this takes plenty of time. The hawk must learn to perch on the gloved fist, which in the beginning should hold food at all times, until it grows accustomed to feeding there. One should never stare directly at a newly acquired hawk. A fixed gaze is characteristic of most predators and generally precedes attack. Hawks seem to understand this, and it creates a lasting impression often difficult to erase.

Any passage redtail should be flying free to the falconer's commands within two weeks after capture. During this time it will have been carried on the fist for several hours each day. There is no sub-

Adult redtail flies to falconer.

stitute for carrying—merely holding the hawk will not suffice. It must become accustomed to the movements of the falconer and this cannot be accomplished without walking.

There is no substitute for experience in learning falconry. Many excellent books on the subject are available which describe in detail the training of a hawk. But all the books in the world can fail to make a falconer. Falconry is an exacting art, let there be no mistaking this. It is almost essential that the novice serve an apprenticeship under the supervision of experienced men. Any one of a thousand seemingly insignificant incidents can upset a hawk, resulting in a loss of many days or even weeks of tedious training; or even of the bird. Unless one can do a hawk justice, it should not be removed from the wild state to begin with.

Fall

MAN HAS LONG PONDERED the migration of birds. A familiar passage in the Bible notes the regularity of the seasonal going and coming: "Yea, the stork in the heaven knoweth her appointed times; and the turtle [dove] and the crane and the swallow observe the time of their coming."

Bird migration has always been intriguing to man—a riddle that is shrouded in mystery. How do they find their way? Do mountain ranges, river courses, coastlines, and other geographical landmarks remain fixed in their minds to lead them back to the land of their ancestry in spring? Do they use the stars and other planets, and the position of the sun, in charting their journey? Do they make use of the earth's magnetic field? . . .

Throughout the ages, many answers have been offered. Aristotle acknowledged that some birds migrate, but went on to state that a great number of them go into hiding. He even suggested transmutation, pointing out that the robin changed into a redstart at the approach of summer. For 2,000 years countless uncritical authors echoed these speculations without question. An exception is the Holy Roman emperor Frederick II, probably the only serious student of migration in his day. His treatise, *The Art of Falconry*, written early in the 13th century, includes 11 chapters on this subject. In recent years some rather startling discoveries have been made about the abilities of some birds to approach the state of hibernation, possibly as a means of overcoming the necessity to migrate. In southeastern California, Dr. Jaeger recently found a whippoorwill in advanced torpor. It was kept under observation for four successive winters, and once remained inactive for 88 days. During this period its body temperature dropped to 64.6 degrees F.

Torpidity has also been observed in such birds as nighthawks, hummingbirds and swifts, although these birds do perform lengthy migrations. Their ability to enter into this state of inactivity has obvious advantages, and enables them to survive unseasonably cold periods.

The ultimate reason that birds migrate apparently lies in the evolutionary adaption by selection to the breeding cycle, and the availability of food. The impetus for migration seems to lie entirely in physiological factors, and certain weather conditions will either trigger the movement, or cause it to cease.

Fall hawk migration has been studied at a number of locations in the East, and has been correlated with the following weather conditions: (*a*) west or northwest winds, (*b*) low pressure system to the north, (*c*) decrease in temperature, (*d*) rising barometer, (*e*) cold front passage. Since these weather conditions often occur together, it is sometimes hard to determine which one, or several in combination, is responsible for initiating the flight.

Spectacular hawk flights occur at several places each fall, the most famous being Cape May, New Jersey; Hawk Mountain, Pennsylvania; and Cedar Grove, Wisconsin. The Milwaukee Public Museum operated a hawk banding station at Cedar Grove for a number of years prior to World War II. This effort to probe the mystery of hawk migration was resumed by Helmut Mueller and Daniel Berger in 1952, and their studies are still in progress. A banding program has never been attempted at Hawk Mountain, where a good deal could be learned, but Chester Robertson and John Holt have recently undertaken a banding program a few miles north of the sanctuary and are beginning to accumulate important data on the movements of Eastern birds.

The concentration of redtails and other hawks which fly south

Hawk banding station in eastern Pennsylvania.

around the western shore of Lake Michigan and over Cedar Grove is a result of the hawk's reluctance to fly over a wide expanse of water. Good hawk flights occur there, almost invariably, when the wind is from a westerly quarter, causing the south-bound migrants to drift east. Encountering the lake shore, they check their drift and proceed to follow the shore line. Easterly winds, on the other hand, result in a poor hawk flight at this location.

At a place like Hawk Mountain, concentrations of hawks are the result of optimum flying conditions along the windward side of a mountain ridge. Powerful updrafts are created when the wind strikes against the flanks of the ridge and is deflected upward. Redtails especially are well designed for this style of flight and can float along for miles without a flap of the wings.

Banding three-week-old hawk.

Glider pilots have long known about red-tailed hawks and their use of updrafts and thermals as a means of easy soaring. Accordingly, a wise pilot is quick to guide his craft toward the path of a soaring hawk. In 1937, Lewin B. Barringer guided his high-performance sailplane on the updrafts along Kittatinny Ridge for 160 miles, from Ellenville, New York, to near Harrisburg, Pennsylvania. Usually when a glider enters a thermal occupied by a soaring redtail the hawk departs without protest. Occasionally, however, an old resident bird may resent such an invasion of its rights and may even attack the aircraft. Mr. David Weller, of the Schweizer Soaring School at Elmira, New York, offers an interesting report of an Eastern redtail that attacked his glider:

"In answer to your questions, yes, it was a red-tailed hawk. It took place about the middle of June around 10 o'clock in the morning. The hawk—we think it was the same hawk—had attacked sailplanes on several occasions during the preceding two weeks. These attacks took place under 2,000 feet over the ridge that is just south of the airport. (Hills and woods.) The hawk always stayed above the sailplane, except when it dove to attack. He seemed to gain altitude for

93

the sole purpose of diving at the sailplane. He made his passes head-on
at the glider, or he would fly along just above and behind the wing.
We never got to enter a thermal with him. On his first attack that
day, he was about 1,000 feet above and 1,500 feet away when he folded
his wings and came down at us. He would pass as close as two feet
from the canopy and we could hear his cry. A possible reason for the
attacks might be that he was protecting a nest near by."

The first migratory movements of redtails in fall are comprised
of young birds of the year. If the individual hawk enjoyed early success in learning to fare for himself, he may begin his wanderings in
late summer. Young redtails from more southern latitudes may often
move a considerable distance north during this period. Whether or not
the young are finally driven away from the home range by their parents
is almost impossible to determine. I personally feel that the majority
depart of their own accord, in response to a physiological stimulus that
occurs when they find themselves self-sufficient.

However, birds in poor condition may be unable to respond and
may linger on. These individuals are almost certainly driven off eventually by their parents, probably in October when the influx of migrants from the north prompts the adult pair to defend the range.
Where the adult birds from the northerly ranges tend to migrate also,
the young probably are only chased away from the favorite hunting
areas.

At the mountain flyway, peak numbers of redtails travel along
the ridges from late October through most of November. The heaviest
hawk flights are generally preceded by meteorological disturbances in
the northern Appalachian regions. Low pressure systems advancing
across these areas appear to start the hawks flying. At Cedar Grove,
passage of a low and its associated cold front also produces a flight.

As can easily be seen on the map showing dispersal of the banded
redtails, the northern birds are highly migratory and may travel between 1,000 and 2,000 miles. An appreciable number of Canadian

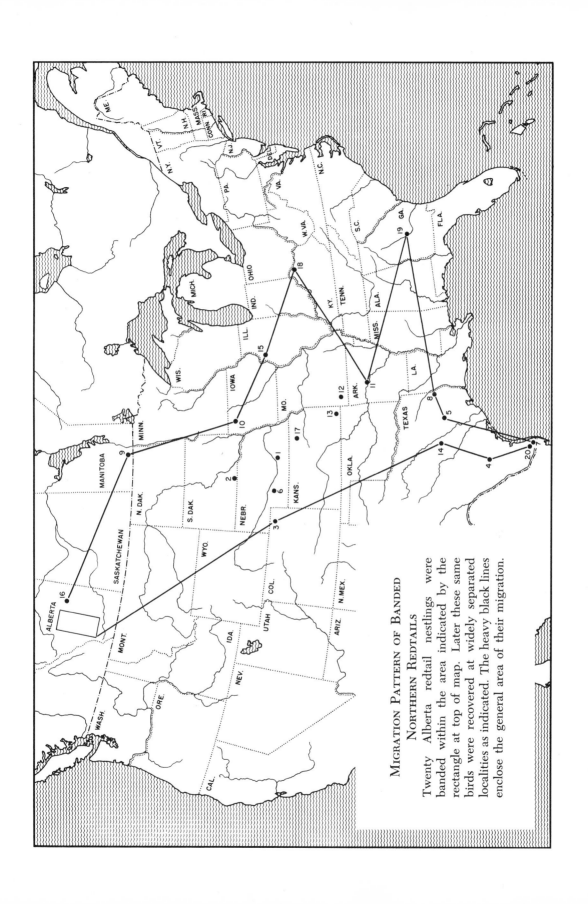

MIGRATION PATTERN OF BANDED
NORTHERN REDTAILS

Twenty Alberta redtail nestlings were
banded within the area indicated by the
rectangle at top of map. Later these same
birds were recovered at widely separated
localities as indicated. The heavy black lines
enclose the general area of their migration.

birds span the continental United States and appear to stop only when they encounter the Gulf of Mexico. Whether these individuals would have returned to the land of their origin had they not met their fate, or whether they represent expendable surplus, is open to speculation.

Spring and summer recoveries of young redtails indicate a strong tendency in the birds to return to the vicinity of their nests, but there is no real proof that these individuals ever moved any great distance to begin with. It is only through concerted banding programs that these and other questions will ever be answered.

Shooting continues to be the major source of recovery for redtails, and the data acquired in this manner only create another point on the map. The hawk thus begins and ends, but we learn nothing about its movements in between. When more redtails wear leg bands, and more banders initiate trapping stations, a great deal will be learned about hawk migration. The recovery data of a single redtail, retrapped several times during its life at different seasons, would be worth more than a hundred "shot" recoveries.

Some of the minor hazards encountered along the way by migrating redtails include exhaustion, electrocution from electric wires, and mangling from trains and automobiles. Obtaining food is an ever-present problem, but primarily a redtail must avoid hunters with shotguns if it is to survive. When one considers that 853 recoveries represent only a minute fraction of the total red-tailed hawk population and that at least 612 of these fell to the gun, as did most of the 136 found dead, the total number of these hawks that have been destroyed by man must be a staggering figure. The majority of banded hawks that are shot are never reported, in most cases because the hunter fears prosecution. Many others, perhaps the majority, fall to the high-powered rifle of the roadside shooter, the most worthless scum of our society, who never retrieves his targets but leaves them to lie where they fall.

Barring interference from man, starvation remains the most seri-

Unsuspecting immature bird, hunting along a highway.

ous hazard confronting migrant redtails, especially those on their first journey. Once a young bird successfully manages this ordeal its chances for living to the next year are greatly increased. Migrants are always at the mercy of an uncertain food supply in the new areas where they find themselves. The more experienced birds seem to be able to recognize productive habitat by its outward appearance alone and do not frequent areas that are obviously low in prey abundance. Two-year-old birds are also much wiser to the ways of man and less likely to be shot. They tend to avoid perching close to the traveled highways, especially the tops of utility poles so frequently chosen by the unwary and unsuspecting immature birds.

All along the route, where the migrant redtails enter the ranges of the resident pairs, the migrants are escorted along by these birds

97

Female sharp-shinned hawk harassing male peregrine falcon during migration.

and are not permitted refuge if they attempt to alight. Temporary refuge may be gained when a resident pair are forced to remain hunting instead of defending their range, but stable birds are usually in good condition and, with them, eating is secondary to keeping the range free of intruders. Migrants usually fly between 10 A.M. and 3 P.M., which leaves ample time for the residents to hunt, anyway.

Although migrants seldom accept the challenge of a defending resident, I witnessed last year the refusal of an immature redtail to hasten its passage over the home range of the resident pair that we were keeping under observation. The old female easily overtook the passing intruder in a long, fast glide at about 2,000 feet. But instead of hurrying away, the young bird rolled over on its back and thrust out its talons. The two simultaneously locked talons and began struggling as they fell. Gaining momentum in the descent, the young hawk attempted to free itself and succeeded in pulling one foot free. But the old female held fast with the other, and both birds tumbled over and over on their way to earth, like a great pinwheel with four flapping wings. Just as I expected to see them crash through the treetops, the old bird appeared to release her grip and the startled youngster vacated the area without further delay. It looked as though the old female had every intention of taking the intruder down to the ground, where she probably would have tried to kill him, but was unable to right herself in the air and hence unwilling to risk ending up in an unfavorable position on the ground. The old male was in evidence all this while but made no effort to assist his mate.

Live trapping for banding purposes of redtails on migration is a challenging occupation for the enthusiastic field worker. At the present time only a handful of trappers band more than a hundred redtails each season. Catching this many birds requires a lot of time and thus becomes a full-time occupation over a two-month period. Most banders have free time only on week ends and may be able to leg-band only 10 or 15 birds; but every bird counts. The novice will experience considerable difficulty in luring redtails all the way in to his trap, but will improve as he works at it.

There are a number of successful methods for catching redtails. Along a mountain ridge, an acre of cleared ground near the crest offers a likely situation for a trapping station. A blind is constructed along the southern edge of the clearing and made to look as inconspicuous as possible. Looking out from the blind, the trapper can spot the oncoming birds.

The common pigeon makes a good lure bird when fitted with a protective leather jacket having holes cut to accommodate the wings.

Hungry immature hawk diving for bait.

The jacket also serves as a harness which keeps the lure from flying away. A six-foot pole is driven vertically into the ground about 50 feet from the blind and a bow trap is placed between the pole and the blind, about 10 feet from the pole.

The lure string is an endless line that runs from the blind to the center of the bow trap where it passes through an eye, out to the top of the pole, back to the ground through an eye, and finally back to the blind. The lure bird (pigeon) is tied onto this line between the trap and the pole.

At the approach of a hawk the lure bird is lifted off the ground briefly, by drawing in the one side of the line. This raises the pigeon toward the top of the pole and results in wing flapping. As soon as the pigeon flaps once or twice, the trapper brings it back to the center of the bow. A hawk that is within human vision can easily spot this action and if hungry will start in immediately, thinking an injured pigeon is easily available. Sometimes even hawks with full crops will respond to the lure, stimulated by the prospect of an easy meal.

Fall

A continuous supply of pigeons is necessary for trapping any large number of hawks. Pigeons soon become conditioned and learn to freeze at the approach of a redtail on the horizon. When lifted off the ground, they simply refuse to open their wings. The only thing to do is change pigeons. It is always wise to keep the tethered pigeons well supplied with food, by scattering grain around the area of the bow. On warm days, a shallow pan of water should be available.

Another method of trapping, sometimes more productive, involves the use of mist nets in front of and behind the lure. Most of the hawks are taken in the front net as they drive for the pigeon, but a number of redtails only make a close pass at the bait, coming in high and missing the front net. Many of these strike the back-up net while pulling up from the dive. The use of nets eliminates the need of keeping a large number of pigeons on hand, because, with the nets, the pigeons are seldom touched by the hawks and do not learn to freeze. The bow trap can also be used in conjunction with the nets to take the occasional hawk that eludes the nets and manages to seize the bait.

Hawk trapping is exciting business but it is filled with frustrations. On the mountain flyway, a good flight of 400 to 500 redtails might net only four or five captures, whereas a poor flight of 50 to 100 birds often

Migrant redtail about to be caught in bow trap.

Just caught in mist net.

produces twice as many bandings. Heavy flights generally occur with changing weather conditions that start the birds flying on the favorable winds. Having been grounded for one or more days, the majority are fed up and are more interested in taking advantage of the optimum flying conditions, reluctant to leave the updrafts. A small percentage of potential bandings are spoiled by the resident hawks which also go aloft on the updrafts, possibly for the sole purpose of watching over their territory. Migrants that respond to the lure are often intercepted by the resident hawks and chased away before reaching the trap.

The adults are always more difficult to catch than the immature migrants. One may expect to take 9 out of 10 immature redtails that

103

Removing redtail from bow trap.

start in as against perhaps 5 out of 10 adults. This is because the young birds are less suspicious and also are in worse condition. The old residents are the most difficult of all; I should be happy to get one out of 10. All redtails seem to "lure in" equally, but the final 50 feet is the moment of truth. The old residents begin sheering away at that distance, to pull up and hang motionless 30 feet in the air. These are the frustrating moments of hawk trapping. Peeping through the tiny hole in the front of the blind, the trapper watches helplessly while the crafty old hawk stares inscrutably in his direction, quietly evaluating the presence of nets, poles, lines . . . and the pigeon that is clad in a garment like a man!

Wise old adult inspecting trapping station.

Winter

EVEN THOUGH fall migration is the rule for immature redtails throughout the major part of the range, exceptions are always interesting to note. Speculation as to why some birds remain behind is most difficult. Two nestlings banded within 10 miles of each other in Michigan are good examples. The first was banded on May 30, 1955, and was recovered on December 3, not more than 60 miles away. The other was banded on May 31, 1955, and was shot in Mississippi on November 24.

It is possible that the bird remaining behind had discovered an area of high prey abundance and that its relatively short migration satisfied the instinctive desire to travel. If the instinct to migrate is based upon the need for food alone, as indeed it appears to be, one might visualize an army of migrating hawks pouring across the continent each fall, dropping off one by one to inhabit environmental niches rich enough in prey species to sustain their needs for a while. An individual redtail might have to move several times over the course of a winter. Another might not have to move at all.

At all seasons the meadow mouse figures rather prominently in the redtail's diet, but in winter this rodent commonly represents the staple prey item. Redtails that have established winter ranges in areas of high mouse density seem to tolerate the presence of rival mousers, such as marsh and rough-legged hawks, early in the season. Later on, if the mice become more difficult to obtain because of heavy snow or other obstacles, the stronger redtails tend to defend their range and drive off the weaker birds.

106

Winter

In my park area where seven resident pairs occupy permanent home ranges, there still remain a few restricted places of less than 50 acres that none of the residents claim. Invariably, each year in late October or early November, a migrant redtail shows up in these areas and usually remains until February or March.

After repeated buffeting about by the old birds, the migrants soon learn their range restrictions. A short flight of some few hundred yards in any direction may bring immediate response from the nearby residents. All the restricted areas are adjacent to, or intersected by, roads, so these wintering hawks are rather easy to trap and band.

In recent years, winter trapping of hawks has become a major week-end activity of many bird banders. Aside from the scientific aspects, it is one of the most engaging winter sports in which a person can participate. It is comparable to hunting, but the quarry is one of the wariest of all and must be stalked carefully, with infinitely more patience than a hunter habitually employs. An idiot can aim and fire a rifle, but it takes considerable doing to outwit a redtail and catch him alive.

A favorite device for winter trapping of redtails is the Bal-chatri trap, or noose cage. The greatest advantage of this trap lies in its portability. Noose cages vary in size and shape, according to the type of hawk to be caught, and the kind of bait to be used.

Half-inch hardware cloth is a good all-round material to build the cage for redtail use, roughly two feet long, one foot wide, and about six inches in height, dome shaped on top. The wire is painted flat black to minimize reflection. Seventy to eighty nooses, each about $1\frac{1}{2}$ inches in diameter, are tied on the dome. Limp-type monofilament fishing line of 25- to 30-pound test strength is used. Line carrying the brand name STREN has proved superior to all others I have tried.

Starlings are excellent bait, but only when they are kept in top condition. Nutritious feeding and snug roosting perches will keep starlings alive and healthy all season. Dried or canned dog food is an ex-

Banding a redtailed hawk.

Band on redtail's leg.

Releasing two redtails after banding.

cellent staple for them. They also require a constant supply of fresh water, for drinking as well as for frequent bathing. Apples are greatly relished and most table scraps are greedily consumed.

When traveling the back roads by auto in search of a hunting redtail, the trap is in readiness on the back seat, and contains two starlings, half an apple, a chunk of suet, and a slice of bread. Without food, the starlings would soon exhaust themselves trying to get out of the cage. The food serves to keep them occupied and at the same time retains their strength. In trapping nothing is more useless than a tired bait.

If a hawk is found perched on a hunting post within 400 feet of the road, we slow the car, open the door on the opposite side from the hawk, and heave the trap onto the rim of the road. It is best never to completely stop the car, nor to let the hawk see the trap leave the car. The trappers then proceed down the road with a gradual increase in speed, so as not to arouse the suspicions of the bird. Five hundred to six hundred feet is ordinarily a safe distance at which to stop and turn around.

Exceptionally keen redtails, when the weather is bitterly cold, will spot the caged starlings at once and be after them, striking at the top of the cage without hesitation. Their feet become snared by the nooses in a matter of seconds. The weight of the trap should be about 24

Snared on noose cage.

ounces, just above the carrying capacity of the hawk, but light enough to be dragged along the ground. During mild periods, redtails are sometimes quite difficult to take on a noose cage, tending to be suspicious of it. In general, adults are always more wary of alighting on top of a noose cage than are birds of the year.

Once a redtail has been taken on a noose cage the chances of ever retrapping the same individual by the same means are slim. They have excellent memories. I have tried repeatedly to retrap banded birds but have succeeded only once; that time by mistake. The bird was a large immature female that arrived in the dead of winter along with a number of other redtails and invaded the area on the heels of a severe storm. She was first trapped around noon, along the road bordering a 50-acre field of corn stubble. At midafternoon we tried for another redtail along the road at the far end of the same field and were surprised to catch the same hawk.

A few days later an adult female was found to be occupying one of the restricted areas in the park that was already inhabited by an immature male. The young bird had gone unbanded because of a trap malfunction earlier in the season, so the arrival of a new period of cold weather prompted another try for him. He was taken without delay on this attempt, while the adult female looked on from only 200 feet. I drove up quickly, took the youngster off the trap and tucked him under an arm, then slowly backed away. The female was taken less than a minute later—one of those very dark individuals that are seen in the area only in winter.

During the winter of 1960 I succeeded in trapping the male of the old Timberlakes pair on a noose cage. Both birds responded to the bait, in this case a white mouse, but only the male was venturesome enough to make a close pass. He refused to alight on top of the cage but engaged in repeated hit and run attacks, trying to strike the bait without stopping. In doing so, one toe finally caught an upright noose and the surprised hawk came to an abrupt stop.

The World of the Red-tailed Hawk

He immediately tried to fly off with the cage and succeeded in carrying it several hundred feet. The moment I jumped from the car to run him down the female flew in close overhead and screamed defiantly. Several times, while I was removing her mate from the trap, she swooped down to within a few feet of my head with all the old enthusiasm I had seen her display so often in previous springs, when we had banded her young.

Again, when the female of another resident pair was taken on a noose cage in January 1962, there was no response at all from the male. This female was perched on a snag about 30 feet high overlooking a small patch of cover, some 300 feet off the road. The trap was presented and we stopped in a farm lane a quarter mile down the road to watch the activity through 60-power telescopes. Five minutes elapsed before she dropped off the perch to strike at some quarry beneath her. During that period she had cast momentary glances at the starlings in the noose cage, well aware of their presence. After missing in her attempt, she paused but a few seconds before flying low and direct to the trap and there was snared on her first hit and run effort. The hour was past sunset and her lack of hesitation in striking the trap may have been associated with the ending of day, a last-ditch effort to feed before going to roost. Her behavior prior to capture illustrated the determination of an experienced bird in refusing to be distracted while awaiting a chance at prey known to be freezing near by.

Many other means have been devised for trapping redtails live, for the hawk bander must always have a number of different methods at his disposal for retrapping the same bird. It also helps to use a different approach, and a car of another color. Redtails quickly learn to associate one vehicle with past capture, and do not soon forget it.

The resident hawks are always difficult to take and the experienced trapper waits for severe weather before trying for them. During mild periods, these crafty individuals almost invariably shy away from the best of traps, to alight in the nearest tree and peer down intently.

112

Winter

Once their suspicions have been aroused, few will ever respond again to the same rig; or even to the same bait.

The successful hawk trapper must be imaginative and constantly on the lookout for new methods. My own failure to take a resident melanistic adult over a period of several years finally resulted in the innovation of a modified style of automatic bow trap and a radio-controlled bow trap. Both have since proved very effective in taking suspicious individuals because the entire device can be camouflaged, leaving only the bait in sight.

Winter is the ideal time for making behavior studies of individuals or paired adults, because the trees are devoid of foliage and the hawks tend to use rather conspicuous hunting perches that overlook open fields harboring meadow mice. Hunting perches are seldom used for more than an hour at a time, but on occasion may be occupied for as long as two or three, and sometimes as long as four hours. Certain individuals can be recognized by their plumage, distinguishing marks, peculiar mannerisms, and so on. The casual observer should exercise extreme caution when isolating an individual for study. If the slightest suspicion exists that the redtail under consideration may be one of two or more similar birds, then the study is invalid.

Resident pairs, and some well-established wintering birds, tend to follow rather definite activity patterns each day. Hunting is always the major activity, but does not always begin as soon as the bird leaves the roost in the morning. Unless hard pressed, the hawks are more apt to spend an hour or so preening while taking in the first warming rays of the sun. Resident adults especially seem to engage in excursion flights over much of their territory early in the morning, as if to check it over.

Several favorite hunting areas exist in the winter range and each redtail visits them at regular intervals. Some birds show remarkable consistency in their movements from one hunting area to the next, day after day, and their presence at one particular spot can often be accu-

Hunting perches.

rately predicted according to the hour of the day. Other birds change hunting areas more frequently, depending on their condition. For instance, a hungry hawk is inclined to be restless, because of its anxiety to secure a meal, and will hunt farther afield than his home territory.

Single birds, both adults and immatures that have migrated, are little inclined to defend the winter range during its early establishment. When occupancy becomes prolonged, most adults and occasional immatures often chase away intruders with the same enthusiasm displayed by defending resident pairs on the home range.

Resident adults spend most of their time in close proximity to each other and often are seen perched together, side by side on the same hunting perch. There seems to be no evidence of a pair actually sharing a kill, but when a large prey is taken it is more than likely that when the first hawk has eaten its fill, the other will then partake. Small prey is swallowed whole or in a few large pieces, by only one member of a pair.

114

The extent of the winter range established by migrants, and its duration of use, is governed by a number of factors, but primarily by the abundance and availability of prey. Use of the land to include isolated patches of fallow field, separated by extensive cultivated areas, sometimes creates numerous ranges . . . or one extensive narrow range, according to one's interpretation. Such ranges may be several miles long and are seldom defended.

Redtails habitually congregate around commercial pheasant shooting preserves in winter, to weed the area of crippled and starving pheasants. Old redtails probably learn the futility of chasing healthy birds that have escaped the hunters' shots, and concentrate on the obviously injured ones. Although a redtail may occasionally succeed in taking a healthy pen-reared pheasant away from cover, the odds are always against it, because a pheasant can fly about twice as fast as the hawk.

The albino redtail pictured here was a migrant immature male hawk (age determined after molt) that established a winter range on

115

Albino redtail in new plumage after molt.

a shooting preserve near my home. The range covered approximately 400 acres, and primary hunting activity centered around a heavy cover area where the surviving pheasants took shelter. Dawn to dusk observations were made of this bird's activities for two consecutive days and a part of a third, until he was captured. Although other wintering redtails are always abundant in this river-bottom section, the white hawk persistently drove off all intruders, adult or immature. Before this hawk arrived to dominate the area, and in the years since, numerous redtails shared the preserve as a hunting area and as many as four had been observed perched in the same tree at the same time, just as rough-legged hawks often do.

The white hawk appeared to have developed a technique for hunting pheasants. When approaching the heavy cover area, his flight was always low and direct. With a brief twist of his wings, he would take a stand atop one of the trees in the midst of the cover and remain

116

Hunting goshawk.

perfectly motionless until a pheasant was sighted. Awaiting the proper moment, he would plunge headlong into the cover, in much the same style of a determined goshawk. If unsuccessful, he would quickly return to the original perch and gaze very intently at the area of his miss. If the quarry failed to move again within five minutes, he would seek a new lookout some hundred feet distant and begin watching for new quarry.

117

The World of the Red-tailed Hawk

On one occasion the hawk made repeated unsuccessful attempts at a single location. Then, in what appeared to be a planned diversionary tactic, he took flight in a leisurely manner that his intended victim could not miss seeing, and flew a quarter mile east to perch atop an isolated utility pole surrounded by bare ground devoid of any possible prey. He drew up one foot and sat motionless, taking an interest in nothing, simply biding his time. Ten minutes had passed when, without warning, he dropped straight down off the pole and proceeded to hurry back to the original spot, keeping within five feet of the ground all the way, coming to perch once more in the same tree and again staring intently at the area of his misses. Less than a minute later he caught a pheasant.

This elusive hawk twice evaded capture during the first two days but was finally taken in a mist net on the morning of the third, within five minutes of his arrival from the roost. During all this time, to keep him hungry and interested in our bait, we had flushed him off his quarry whenever he made a kill.

The melanistic redtail pictured here was the male of a resident pair which occupied a choice environment near the beginning of red-shouldered hawk habitat. He was first observed in 1952 when the area came under initial study. The range of this pair was gradually extended each year due to habitat destruction and housing development. The female was not observed after late 1959, but the black hawk remained until late November 1962. Three weeks later he was found 90 miles northeast where he had already established a well-defined winter territory. Tentative identification was made through a number of peculiar behavior traits seldom observed in redtails, and later verified through a 60-power telescope at a distance of 200 feet.

In February 1962, this hawk was caught by a perfectly camouflaged trap after eight years of periodic attempts to capture him. The old age of this bird was reflected by his wisdom in avoiding anything new and strange on his territory. After recording him on film during a

Melanistic adult.

week in captivity, we released him in the park, 15 miles southwest of his home range. Two days later he was back on his home range, where he remained until migrating in November. It is obvious that habitat destruction forced him to leave his original range, but it is difficult to understand why he traveled so far. It is interesting to note, however, that the new territory he chose is an area frequented by the highest concentrations of mouse-eating hawks to be found in the entire state, for the area is an extensive soil-bank reservation rich in meadow mice.

119

The World of the Red-tailed Hawk

On his original home range, the black hawk was more a restricted feeder than a general feeder, no doubt the result of his unusually small feet. He was never observed with any quarry larger than a rat.

The night roost of redtails in winter is usually near a favorite hunting area in a foliated tree such as a cedar or conifer set in the midst of a patch of woodland or a high thicket which offers protection from icy blasts. The limited observations on this phase of the redtails' daily routine suggest that a number of different roosts are used. As indicated by the accumulation of droppings and pellets below the roosts, the hawks do not use the same one for many days or weeks in succession—unlike a number of wintering owls.

Adults are fairly impervious to the elements and can maintain strong flight even after extensive downpours. Immature hawks are usually reluctant to fly when they become saturated, and at such times are all the more vulnerable to the folly of the gunner. Whether the

Adult shaking water from plumage.

Feather damaged by lice. Note that the barbules were eaten only from the whiter area of the feather.

121

adults take better care of their plumage through more active preening, or whether the adult feathers themselves are less inclined to wear, is open to speculation.

Feather parasites may be responsible for a certain percentage of late winter mortality when they infect the bird in abnormal numbers, causing extensive decomposition by eating the barbules. The hawk is thus rendered less maneuverable and adept in catching its prey.

In March, the winter survivors grow restless, and soon the spring migration begins. Breeding adults that have migrated or drifted are presumably the first to arrive back on the home range, to renew old acquaintances and prepare for new families. The younger birds follow to replace those that do not return. Ideally, where man has not intervened, survival of nonbreeding birds barely exceeds the breeding adult mortality each year, assuring continued existence of the species.

At the present time man has become efficient enough, aside from the toll he takes indirectly through habitat destruction, to account for all but a fraction of the 80 to 90 per cent natural annual loss of nonbreeding birds. Viewing the picture objectively, it might even be said that the birds which fall before guns are spared the misery of slow starvation. Nevertheless, as soon as man's efficiency increases enough to wipe out the slim excess of vital "stand-by" birds, mass extermination of redtails over vast areas will speedily follow.

Innocent victim of an indiscriminate killer.

List of Red-tailed Hawk Subspecies

At present, six races are recognized in North America by the American Ornithologists' Union:

Eastern Red-tailed Hawk, *Buteo jamaicensis borealis,* breeds from Mackenzie, across Canada to southern Quebec and Newfoundland, south to central Texas, northeastern Oklahoma, Alabama and northern Florida.

Florida Red-tailed Hawk, *Buteo jamaicensis umbrinus,* smaller and darker than the Eastern bird, inhabits Peninsular Florida, Cuba, and Isle of Pines, it strays occasionally into southern Georgia and, even less frequently, to lower South Carolina.

Krider's Red-tailed Hawk, *Buteo jamaicensis kriderii,* the palest race; some individuals appear to be albinistic Eastern redtails. Krider's redtail breeds from the southern prairie provinces into Wyoming, North Dakota and Minnesota and south to Missouri and Nebraska. Partially albino Eastern birds are sometimes called *kriderii;* and in late winter and early spring immature *borealis* often show considerable plumage wear, fade, and come to resemble *kriderii.*

Fuertes Red-tailed Hawk, *Buteo jamaicensis fuertsi,* the desert race, lives in southwestern Texas. More precise range limits have yet to be determined.

Alaska Red-tailed Hawk, *Buteo jamaicensis alascensis,* lives from Yakutat Bay to the Queen Charlotte Islands.

Western Red-tailed Hawk, *Buteo jamaicensis calurus,* breeds from southeastern Alaska and western Mackenzie south to Lower California and east to the edge of the Great Plains. This race shows wide plumage variation in individuals, tending strongly towards melanism. Some birds are as dark as the black phase of the American rough-legged hawk, except that the red tail is little affected.

Bibliography

Allen, Robert P., and Peterson, Roger T., "The Hawk Migrations at Cape May Point, New Jersey." *The Auk,* October 1936, Vol. LIII, No. 4.

Bent, Arthur Cleveland, *Life Histories of North American Birds of Prey,* Part 1. U. S. National Museum Bulletin 167, Washington, D.C., 1937.

Craighead, Frank C., Jr., and John J., *Hawks, Owls and Wildlife.* The Stackpole Co., Harrisburg, Pa. and Wildlife Management Institute, Washington, D. C., 1956.

Hagar, Donald C., "Nesting Populations of Red-tailed Hawks and Horned Owls in Central New York State." *The Wilson Bulletin,* September 1957, Vol. 69, No. 3.

Ingram, Collingwood, "The Importance of Juvenile Cannibalism in the Breeding Biology of Certain Birds of Prey." *The Auk,* April 1959, Vol. 76, No. 2.

Jones, Glenn, "Hail Damage to Wildlife in Southwest Oklahoma." *The Wilson Bulletin,* September 1952, Vol. 64, No. 3.

Lord, Ford D., "An Anomalous Condition in the Eye of Some Hawks." *The Auk,* July 1956, Vol. 73, No. 3.

Mueller, Helmut C., and Berger, Daniel D., "Weather and Fall Migration of Hawks at Cedar Grove, Wisconsin." *The Wilson Bulletin,* June 1961, Vol. 73, No. 2.

Nakamura, Mitsuru, "Tularemia in the Red-Tailed Hawk." *The Auk,* July 1950, Vol. 67, No. 3.

Peterson, Roger T., and the Editors of *Life, The Birds.* Life Nature Library, Time Inc., 1963.

Pettingill, Olin S., Jr., *A Laboratory and Field Manual of Ornithology.* Burgess Publishing Company, Minneapolis, Minn., 1958.

Sprunt, Alexander, Jr., *North American Birds of Prey.* Harper and Brothers, New York, 1955.

Index

Index

The World of the Red-tailed Hawk